COLORS, SHAPE & TIME

P9-BYE-891

This Workbook and CD-ROM:

Garfield 'It's all about Colors, Shapes, and Time'

Designed for preschool students aged 3-5 years

This Workbook and CD-ROM introduce your child to the concept of Colors, Shapes, and Time. Activities covered include color recognition, shapes and patterns, the basics of understanding time, and many other activities designed to help your child understand each of these topics. Working with both the Workbook and the CD-ROM, your child will be guided through each activity area, and will find Garfield and his Friends close at hand to keep them entertained and interested for hours of fun and learning.

Published on behalf of ESP International Ltd
NSK-ESP Garfield LLC
4636 Lebanon Pike
Hermitage
TN 37076-4708
Tel 615 469 0929
Email: info@NuSpringKids.com
Website: www.NuSpringKids.com

Draw a line from the shape
to its correct name.

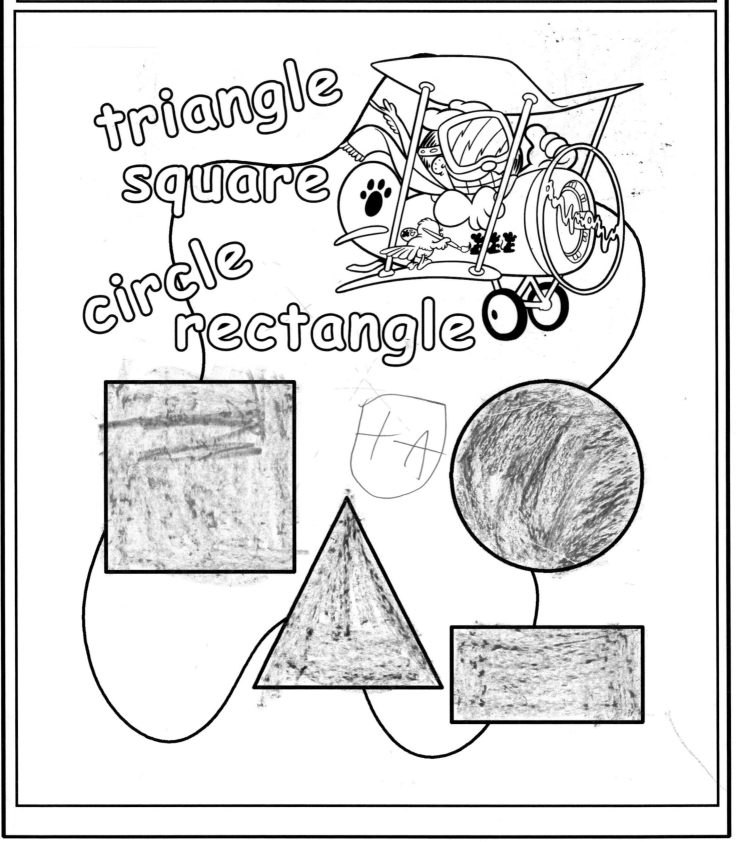

triangle

square

circle

rectangle

COLORS, SHAPES AND TIME.

Draw a line from the big shapes to the correct little shapes in the picture.

Draw the shape that comes next.

A square is a shape that looks like this.

square

How many squares can you see in the picture below?

Write your answer here.

6

COLORS, SHAPES AND TIME.

Color the clock that tells the earliest time.

A circle is a shape that looks like this.

circle

How many circles can you see?

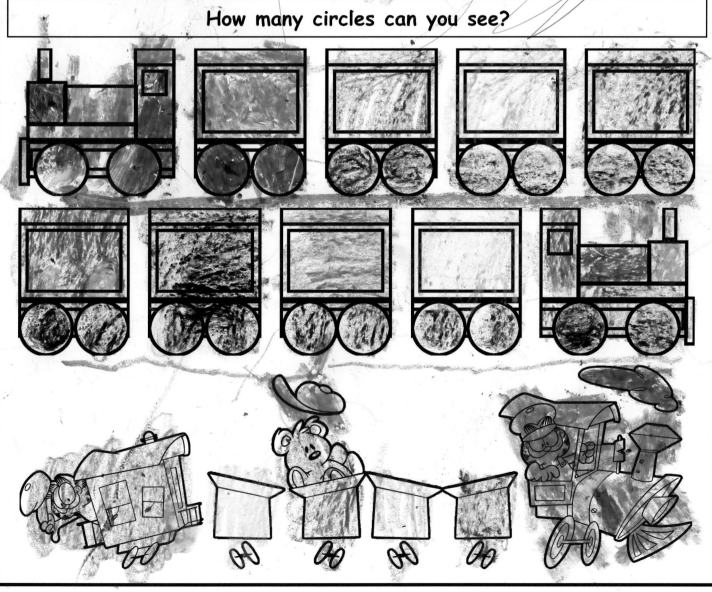

What color would you get if you mixed red and yellow?
Shade the big square with the correct color.

Color the clock that tells the latest time.

COLORS, SHAPES AND TIME.

A rectangle is a shape that
looks like this.

rectangle

How many rectangles can you see?

Write your answer here. 7

How many red clocks can you see?
Put your answer in the box below.

COLORS, SHAPES AND TIME.

Trace the numbers in the clocks.
Make the clocks show 1 and 5 O`clock.

Circle the shape which does not belong in each group.

COLORS, SHAPES AND TIME.

Circle the odd one out.

COLORS, SHAPES AND TIME.

How many green clocks can you see in the picture?
Put your answer in the box below.

21

COLORS, SHAPES AND TIME.

Draw a line from the shapes to the correct objects.

Shapes

Objects

COLORS, SHAPES AND TIME.

Which time is the odd one out?
Write the correct times in the boxes below each clock.

COLORS, SHAPES AND TIME.

Draw the shape that comes next.

Draw a line from the word to the object.

Circle

Triangle

Square

Rectangle

COLORS, SHAPES AND TIME.

Draw a line from the name to the correct color.

red   blue   green   yellow

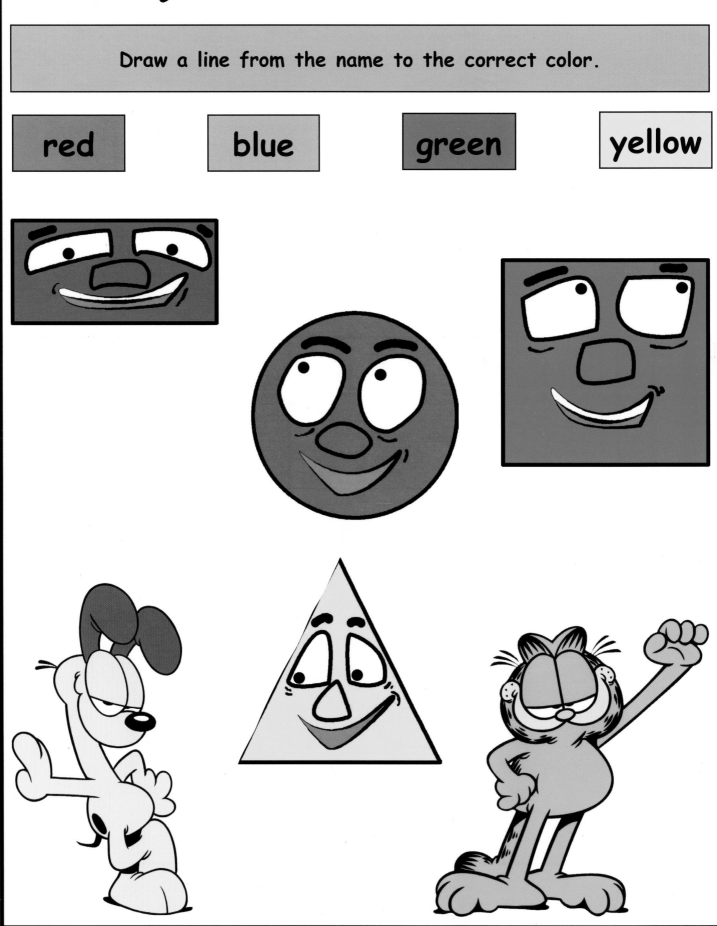

A triangle is a shape that looks like this.

triangle

How many triangles can you see in the picture below?

Write your answer here.

COLORS, SHAPES AND TIME.

Draw the missing shapes.

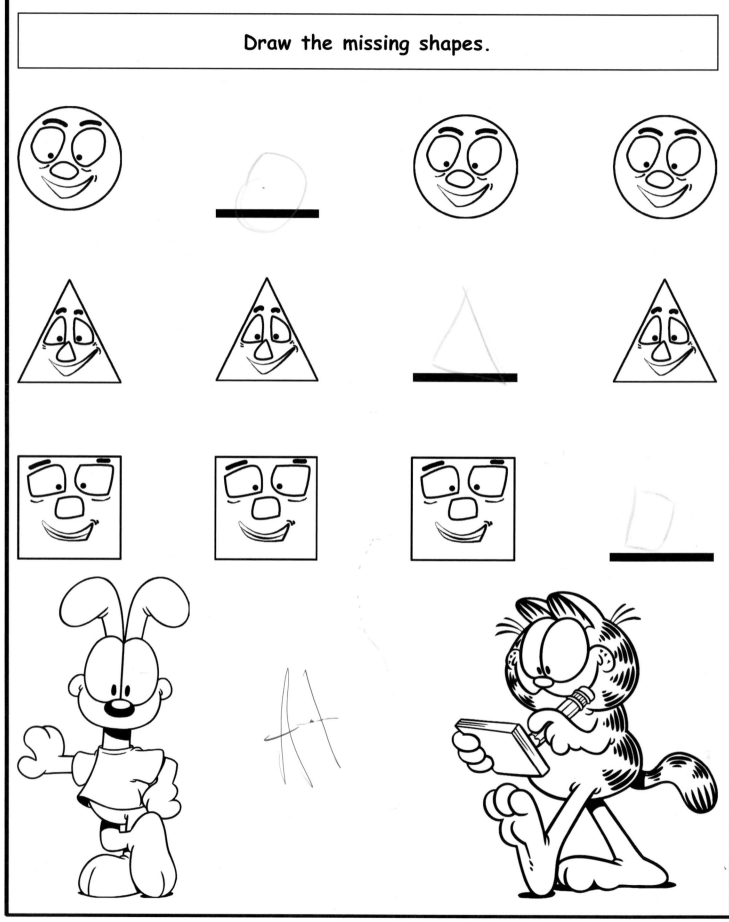

COLORS, SHAPES AND TIME.

Draw a line from the shapes to the correct objects.

Shapes

Objects

COLORS, SHAPES AND TIME.

Color the building that has red doors.